Key Stage 2

Changing Materials

Penny Johnson

Name _____

Schofield & Sims

Introduction

The materials around us can be changed from solids to liquids or gases and back again. For example, some materials are changed when they are heated or added to water. In this book you will learn about how materials can be changed. You will also find out how some changes can be reversed, while others cannot.

How to use this book

Before you start using this book, write your name in the box on the first page.

Then decide how to begin. If you want a complete course on how materials can be changed, you should work right through the book from beginning to end. Another way to use the book is to dip into it when you want to find out about a particular topic. The Contents page or the Index at the back of the book will help you to find the pages you need.

Whichever way you choose, don't try to do too much at once – it's better to work through the book in short bursts.

When you have found the topic you want to study, look out for the icons below which mark different parts of the text.

Finally, use the Scientific investigation table on page 30 to find out how the **Understanding Science** series can help you use your new skills to investigate scientific questions in other topics.

Activities

These are the activities that you should complete. Write your answers in the spaces provided. After you have worked through all the activities on the page, turn to pages 31–35 at the end of the book to check your answers. When you are sure that you understand the topic, put a tick in the box beside it on the Contents page.

Explanation

This text explains the topic and gives examples. Read it before you start the activities. Any words shown like this appear in the combined Index and glossary. Turn to page 36 to see what these words mean.

Did you know?

Information

This text gives you useful background information and interesting facts about the subject.

Contents

There are two books about materials in this series: **Using Materials** and **Changing Materials** (this book). You should work through **Using Materials** before you look at this book, because you need to understand what olids, liquids and gases are before you can learn about how they can be changed.

Melting and solidifying

Ice is a **solid**. It keeps its shape and does not flow.

Water is a **liquid**. It can flow and it takes the shape of whatever container you put it in.

Water and ice are the same material, but each is in a different **state**. Solids and liquids are two different states.

You can change the state of a material by changing its **temperature**. You can melt ice by warming it up. You can freeze (or solidify) water by cooling it down.

Water changes to ice (and ice changes to water) at 0°C. If you leave some ice cubes in a glass, they will melt. The air in the room is warmer than the ice cubes, so heat goes from the air to the ice cubes and they warm up.

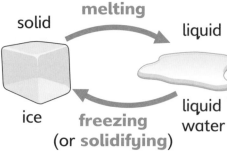

1. Write down the names of two states that materials can be in.

_____

2. a) What is the word that describes a solid changing to a liquid?

_____

b) Write down two words that describe a liquid changing to a solid.

_____

3. Why will ice cubes melt if you leave them in a glass in the kitchen?

_____

4. a) How can you change water into ice?

_____

b) How cold does the water have to be before it starts turning into ice?

_____

Other materials can be melted or frozen, but this happens at different **temperatures**. For example, chocolate will **melt** if you hold it in your hand. You can turn the **liquid** chocolate back into a **solid** by leaving it on a plate to cool.

Some materials need to be much hotter before they will melt. The knives and forks you use when you eat are made from a metal called steel. Steel is normally a solid, but it melts if it is heated to about 1400°C.

Lava is liquid rock. Some places inside the Earth are hot enough to melt rock, and the **molten** rock sometimes comes out of the ground in volcanoes. Rock melts at about 1000°C.

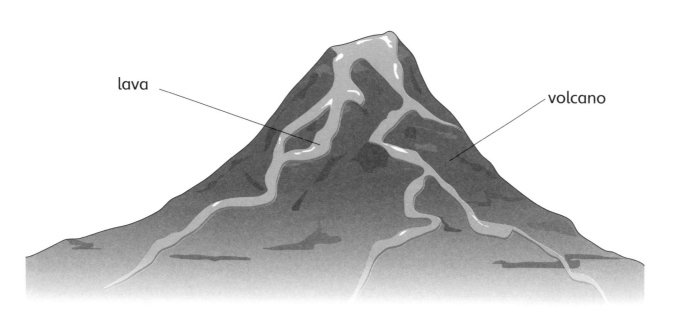

lava

volcano

5. a) Why doesn't butter usually melt if you leave it on a plate in the kitchen?

_____

b) How can you make butter melt?

_____

6. When lava has come out of a volcano, it turns into solid rock again. Why does this happen?

_____

Evaporation and smells

You can see puddles on the ground when it is raining. When it stops raining, the puddles gradually dry up. It looks as if the water in the puddles has disappeared.

The **liquid** water in the puddles has turned into a **gas**. We say that the water has evaporated. The water is still there in the air, but we cannot see it because it has turned into a gas. When water is a gas it is sometimes called **water vapour**.

Evaporation happens faster if the water is warm. This is why puddles dry up faster on a warm day.

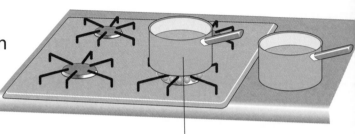

The water in this pan will evaporate faster, because it is warmer.

1. Which word describes a liquid turning into a gas? Tick one box.

☐ melting ☐ evaporating ☐ freezing

2. Why do puddles dry up faster on a warm day?

_____

3. Dina and Jake are talking about puddles drying up.

Dina

The water in the puddle has disappeared.

The water has turned into water vapour.

Jake

Who is right? _____

Did you know? When some of a liquid evaporates the liquid that is left behind is a little cooler. This is why your body sweats when you are too hot. As the sweat evaporates, it makes your body cooler.

Evaporation and smells

Some **liquids** evaporate more easily than water. Aftershave and perfume both evaporate easily. The liquid turns into a **gas** and the gas spreads out through the air in the room. You can smell the perfume when the gas reaches your nose.

When you paint a picture, you need to let the paint dry. Paint is a coloured powder mixed with water. When you spread the paint on to a piece of paper, the water in it starts to evaporate. The paint is dry when all the water has evaporated.

Nail varnish is also a coloured material mixed with a liquid. The liquid in nail varnish evaporates easily when the nail varnish is painted on to fingernails.

4. a) What **state** is perfume in when someone puts it on?

_____

b) What state is perfume in when you smell it? _____

5. What happens when paint dries?

_____

6. How can you tell that nail varnish is drying without touching it?

_____

Investigating evaporation 1

Washing dries when the water in it evaporates.

Class 5 want to find out how to make washing dry faster. They are going to investigate what affects **evaporation**. Something you can investigate in an experiment is called a **variable**. In a **fair test**, you only change one variable at a time.

We could find out if the **temperature** makes a difference.

Things might dry faster if they have a bigger area.

Do you think the wind will make a difference?

1. Write down three different variables that might affect evaporation.

_____

Jane and Will are finding out if area makes a difference to evaporation.

Jane dipped two paper towels in water. She spread one of them out on the table to dry and she folded up the other one. She watched them to see which one dried first.

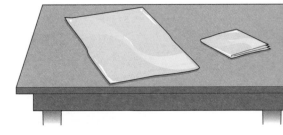

Will poured 50 ml of water into two different tubs and left them near a radiator. Every day for the next five days he carefully poured the water from each tub into a measuring cylinder to see how much was left, then poured it back into the tub again.

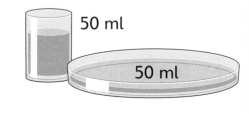

50 ml

50 ml

2. Why is Will's investigation a better scientific test than Jane's?

_____

_____

3. What did Jane have to keep the same to make her test fair?

_____

The table shows Will's results. Will drew a **line graph** to show his results.

Day	Volume of water left (ml)	
	Large area	Small area
0 (start)	50	50
1	40	45
2	30	40
3	20	35
4	10	30
5	0	25

Evaporation investigation

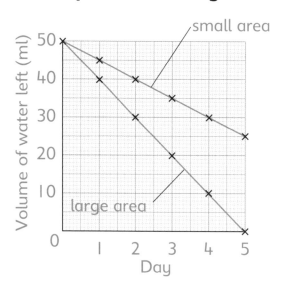

A **conclusion** is when you say what you have found out in an investigation. An **evaluation** is when you say how good your investigation was and if you did a **fair test**. If you can, you should also say if you could make your investigation any better.

4. What do you think Jane found in her investigation? Write a conclusion for Jane.

_____

5. Write a conclusion for Will's investigation. _____

_____

_____

6. Write an evaluation for Will's investigation. _____

_____

_____

Investigating evaporation 2

Becky wanted to find out if the **temperature** affects **evaporation**. She took two jars of water and put one in a warm place and one in a cold place. She measured the depth of the water in each container every day. The table shows her results.

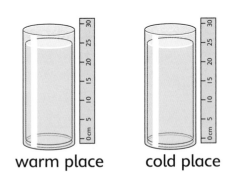

warm place   cold place

Day	Depth of water (mm)	
	Warm place	Cold place
0 (start)	25	25
1	21	23
2	17	21
3	13	19
4	9	17
5	5	15

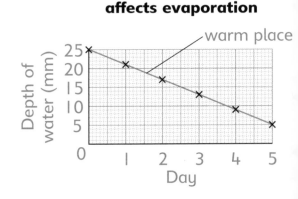

How temperature affects evaporation

Becky drew a **line graph** to show her results.

1. Finish Becky's graph by adding a line for the water in a cold place.

2. Write a **conclusion** for Becky's investigation. _____

_____

_____

3. Write an **evaluation** for Becky's investigation. _____

_____

_____

4. a) Does water evaporate when it is cold? _____

b) How did you work out your answer to part **a)**? _____

_____

Speeding up evaporation

Water evaporates faster when it is warm than when it is cold.

If you spread out something that is drying, there is more area for the water to evaporate from. This makes **evaporation** faster.

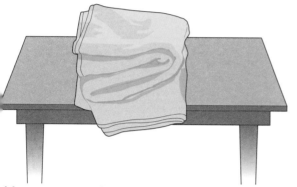

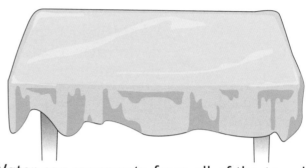

Water can only evaporate from the part of the towel on the outside.

Water can evaporate from all of the towel.

Water also evaporates faster if there is a breeze. When water evaporates, it turns into **water vapour**, which stays in the air. A breeze blows this water vapour away, so that more water can evaporate.

1. Write down three things that can make water evaporate quickly.

_____

2. How does a hairdryer help to dry wet hair quickly? (There are two ways.)

_____

3. a) Which towel will dry faster? _____

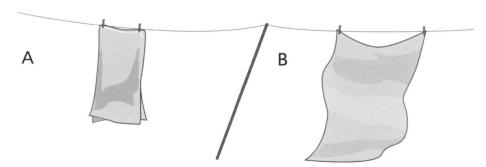

A

B

b) Explain why this towel will dry faster.

_____

_____

Condensation

When a kettle is **boiling**, the water in it is **evaporating** as fast as it can. The water turns into a **gas** called **water vapour**. We cannot see water vapour. The cloud of 'steam' that you can see above the kettle is actually tiny drops of water. The water vapour has cooled down and turned back into a **liquid**. This process is called **condensation**.

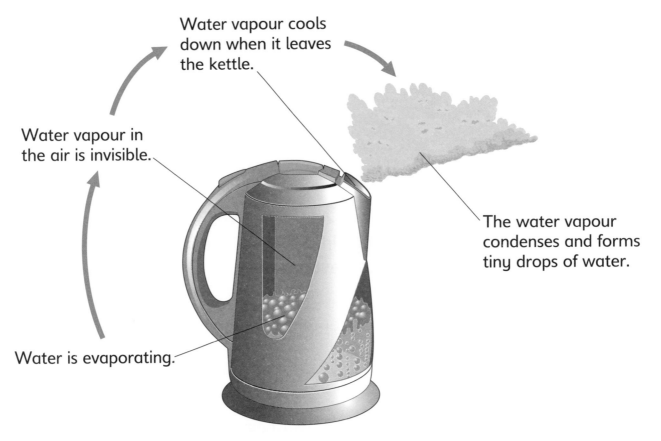

Water vapour cools down when it leaves the kettle.

Water vapour in the air is invisible.

The water vapour condenses and forms tiny drops of water.

Water is evaporating.

This diagram summarises the changes of **state**.

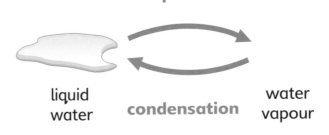

evaporation

liquid water

condensation

water vapour

1. a) Which word describes a gas changing to a liquid? _____

b) Which word describes a liquid changing to a gas? _____

The air around us always has some **water vapour** in it. If the air is cooled down, this water vapour can condense.

When you have a bath or shower, some of the water **evaporates**, so the air in the bathroom has a lot of water vapour in it. Air that touches a cold surface, like a mirror or the window, cools down and the water vapour in it condenses. The water drops on the mirror or the window are also called **condensation**.

condensation

The diagram shows the kitchen in Samir's house.

2. There is lots of water vapour in the air in the kitchen. Where has the water vapour come from?

_____

3. Why are there lots of small drops of water on the window? Explain in as much detail as you can.

_____

_____

4. Why are you more likely to see condensation on windows in the winter than in the summer?

_____

5. Samir took a can of cola out of the fridge. After a couple of minutes he noticed drops of water on the outside of the can. Where has this water come from?

_____

_____

The water cycle

Water goes in a cycle, from the sea to clouds, then to rain, rivers and back to the sea again. These changes are called the **water cycle**. The diagram below shows you how the water cycle works.

We need water for cooking and washing. This water comes to our homes in pipes. In some places, water is taken out of rivers and cleaned before being sent to homes. In other places, water soaks into the ground. We can use this water by digging wells and pumping the water up. Reservoirs can also trap water so it can be used.

Water runs into the drains after we have used it. This waste water is treated in sewage works and then put back into rivers or into the sea.

Did you know? Astronauts on the Space Station drink recycled water. Water from washing and from toilets is collected and cleaned before being used again.

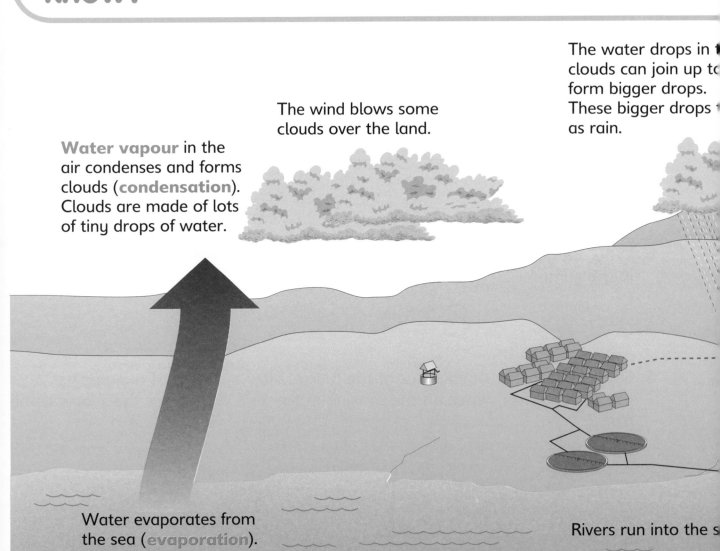

The water drops in the clouds can join up to form bigger drops. These bigger drops as rain.

The wind blows some clouds over the land.

Water vapour in the air condenses and forms clouds (**condensation**). Clouds are made of lots of tiny drops of water.

Water evaporates from the sea (**evaporation**).

Rivers run into the s

The water cycle

1. a) How does water get into the air from the sea?

_____

b) Where else could this happen?

_____

2. What happens when water in the air **condenses**?

_____

3. What happens to rain when it falls?

_____

4. Why are these changes called the **water cycle**?

_____

5. Write down two different places that the water in our taps could come from.

_____

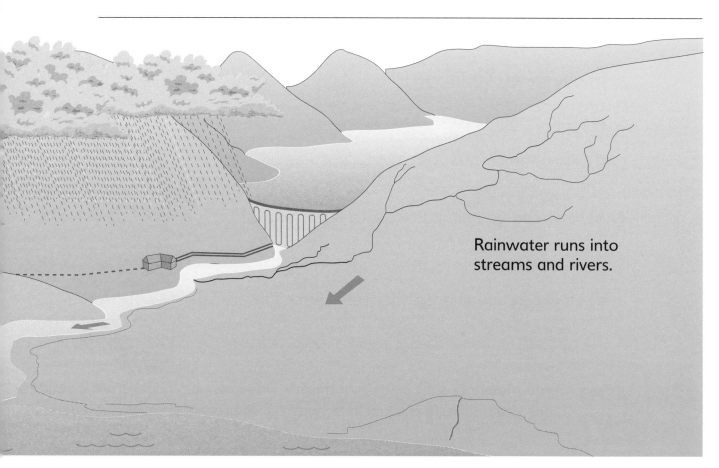

Rainwater runs into streams and rivers.

Changing state

Many materials can exist in three **states: solid, liquid** or **gas**. You can make materials change state by changing the **temperature**.

A change of state is a **reversible change**. This means that if you change ice into water by warming it up, you can change the water back into ice by cooling it down.

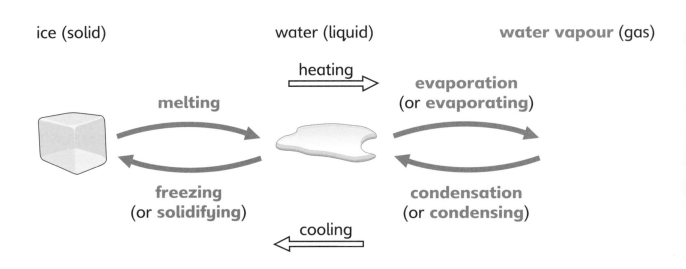

ice (solid)   water (liquid)   **water vapour** (gas)

heating

melting

**evaporation
(or evaporating)**

**freezing
(or solidifying)**

**condensation
(or condensing)**

cooling

1. Write the correct words next to each of these changes:

a) liquid ⟶ solid _____

b) gas ⟶ liquid _____

c) solid ⟶ liquid _____

d) liquid ⟶ gas _____

2. a) How can you change ice into liquid water?

_____

b) How can you change the water back into ice?

_____

Did you know? Some materials, such as carbon dioxide, can change straight from a solid to a gas without being a liquid in between. This process is called sublimation.

Changing state

Evaporation can happen at any **temperature**, but it happens faster at higher temperatures. If you heat water to 100°C, it starts to boil. In **boiling** water, evaporation is happening so fast that bubbles of **water vapour** start to form inside the liquid. The water will not get any hotter than 100°C, even if you carry on heating it.

The graph shows how the temperature of ice changes if you put it into an oven.

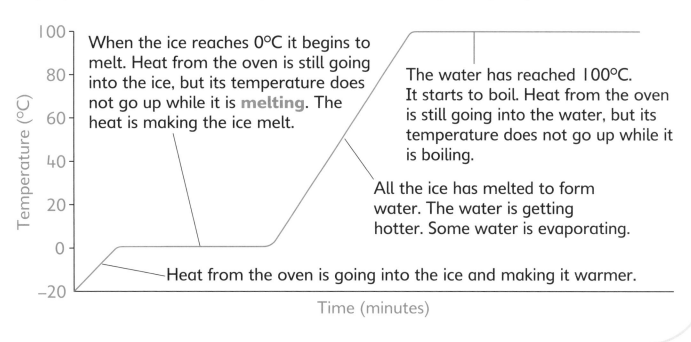

When the ice reaches 0°C it begins to melt. Heat from the oven is still going into the ice, but its temperature does not go up while it is **melting**. The heat is making the ice melt.

The water has reached 100°C. It starts to boil. Heat from the oven is still going into the water, but its temperature does not go up while it is boiling.

All the ice has melted to form water. The water is getting hotter. Some water is evaporating.

Heat from the oven is going into the ice and making it warmer.

3. a) At what temperature does ice start to melt? _____

b) At what temperature does water start to boil? _____

c) At what temperature does water start to evaporate?

(Hint: this is not the same answer as part **b)**!) _____

4. a) What happens to the temperature of ice while it is melting?

_____

b) What happens to the temperature of water when it is boiling?

_____

5. What is inside the bubbles you can see when water is boiling?

_____

Separating mixtures

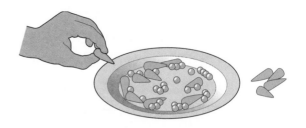

Chloë has a bag of peas and carrots. The peas and carrots are a **mixture**. She can separate the mixture by picking the carrots out with her fingers.

You can use a sieve to help you to separate some mixtures. A sieve has holes in it that are big enough for some of the things in the mixture to go through. Bigger objects get trapped in the sieve. You can use a sieve to separate a mixture of marbles and water, but you cannot use one to separate sand and water.

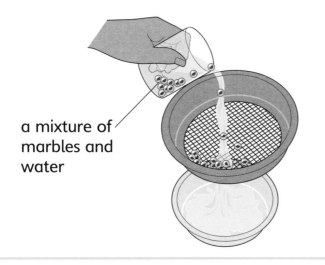

a mixture of marbles and water

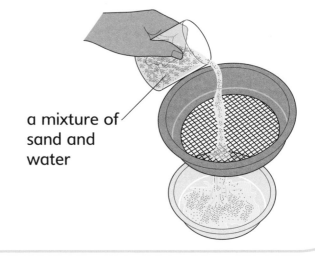

a mixture of sand and water

1. a) How can you separate a mixture of buttons and marbles?

_____

b) Why can't you use this method to separate sand and water?

_____

2. Why hasn't the sieve in the diagram separated the sand from the water?

_____

Did you know? Milk is a mixture of two **liquids**. It is made of tiny drops of fat mixed with water. There are some other chemicals **dissolved** in the water that stop the fat and the water separating.

To separate a **mixture**, you need a sieve with holes that are big enough to let one part of the mixture through, but not big enough to let the other part through.

Filter paper is special paper that has very tiny holes in it. The holes are too small to see. Kitchen towel also has very tiny holes in it. You can use this kind of paper to separate sand and water. This is called **filtering**. The water goes through the holes in the paper, but the grains of sand are too big to go through the holes. The sand is trapped in the paper.

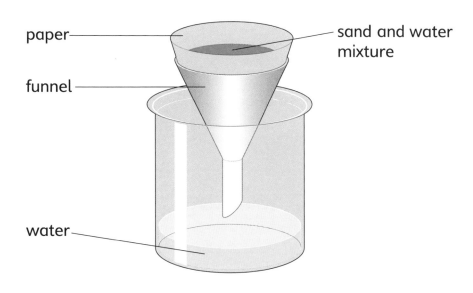

paper — sand and water mixture

funnel

water

3. Why does the sand get trapped in the paper?

_____

4. Finish these sentences to explain what happens.

a) You can use a sieve to separate flour and dried peas because

_____

_____

b) You cannot use a sieve to separate flour and sand because

_____

_____

Some **solids** seem to disappear when you mix them with water. For example, if you put sugar in water, the sugar seems to disappear. If you taste the water, you can tell that the sugar is still there because the water tastes sweet. Sugar will **dissolve** in water. The **mixture** of sugar and water is called a **solution**. A solution is transparent, so you can see through it. Some solutions are coloured, but you can still see through them.

When a solid dissolves in water it splits up into very tiny pieces that mix with the water. The pieces are so small that you cannot see them. They are also small enough to go through the holes in filter paper, so you cannot separate the parts of a solution by **filtering**.

Flour does not dissolve in water. You cannot see through a mixture of flour and water.

Black tea is a coloured solution.

Sugar dissolves in water to make a colourless solution.

1. a) Salt dissolves in water. What word used above describes a mixture of salt and water? _____

b) What does a mixture of salt and water look like?

_____

2. How can you tell that flour does not dissolve in water?

_____

3. Complete the table to show what happens when you try to filter the following mixtures. The first one has been done for you.

Mixture	What is left in the filter paper	What goes through the filter paper
sugar and water	nothing	sugar and water
sand and water		
flour and water		
salt and water		

Dissolving

If you leave a **solution** of sugar and water for long enough, the water will evaporate. Only the **liquid** can evaporate, so anything that was **dissolved** in the liquid will get left behind. You can make the **evaporation** faster by heating the solution.

f **water vapour** that has evaporated from a solution of sugar and water hits a cold surface, it will condense and form liquid water. This water will not taste sweet, because there is no sugar in it.

Dissolving is a **reversible change**, because you can separate the two parts of the **mixture** again.

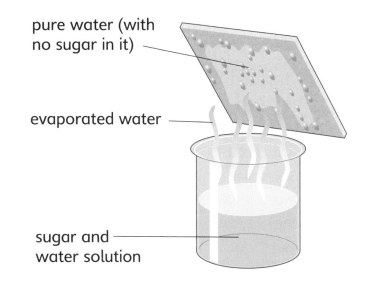

pure water (with no sugar in it)

evaporated water

sugar and water solution

4. Muhammad mixes some salt with some water.

   a) What happens to the salt? _____

   b) Why can't Muhammad get the salt back by **filtering** the solution?

   _____

5. Muhammad heats the solution and holds a cold tile above the beaker to make the water vapour condense.

   a) Will the condensed water taste salty? _____

   b) Explain your answer to part **a)**. _____

   _____

   _____

Did you know? Your taste buds detect the chemicals in solutions. This means that you can only taste things that are dissolved in water or dissolve in the saliva in your mouth.

Dissolving faster

Class 6 are finding out how to make sugar **dissolve** faster in water. They use the same amount of sugar for each experiment.

Dan found out that stirring the **mixture** made the sugar dissolve faster. The **bar chart** shows his results. He used a bar chart because he could describe the **variable** that he changed in words: 'stirring' and 'no stirring'.

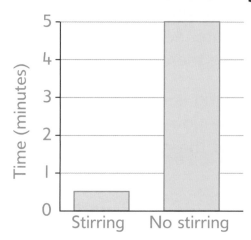

Dissolving sugar with and without stirring

Ellie investigated the **temperature** of the water. She used water at four different temperatures. The **line graph** shows her results. Ellie used a line graph because the factor she was changing is a measurement, and there are numbers between her measurements that mean something. For example, she could have used water at 25°C and she would have found that the sugar dissolved in 9 seconds.

Chloë investigated the sizes of the pieces of sugar. She used caster sugar (with very small pieces), normal sugar and sugar lumps. The table shows her results.

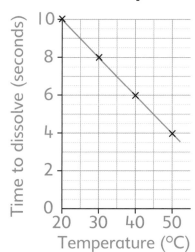

Dissolving sugar at different temperatures

Sugar	Time to dissolve (seconds)
caster	20
normal	30
lumps	80

1. What variables did Dan have to keep the same to make sure his test was f

_____

_____

2. What variables did Ellie have to keep the same?

_____

3. Cross out the incorrect words in this sentence.

You can make sugar dissolve faster by stirring/not stirring it, by using bigger/smaller pieces and by putting it in hotter/colder water.

4. a) Should Chloë use a **bar chart** or a **line graph** to show her results?

_____

b) Explain your answer to part **a)**.

_____

_____

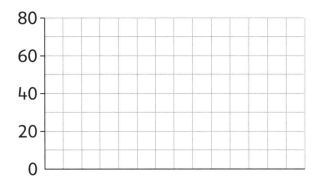

c) Show Chloë's results on this grid.

5. Ali investigated how fast salt **dissolved** at different **temperatures**. The table shows his results.

Temperature of water (°C)	Time for salt to dissolve (seconds)
20	25
30	20
40	15
50	10

a) Should Ali use a bar chart or a line graph to show his results?

_____

b) Explain your answer to part **a)**.

_____

_____

_____

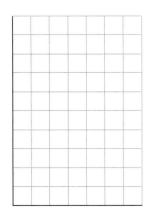

c) Show Ali's results on this grid.

How much will dissolve?

Sophie wanted to find out how much sugar would **dissolve** in water. She put a scoop of sugar into water and stirred it until it had all dissolved. She kept putting more sugar in and stirring, until she could see that there was some sugar in the water that did not dissolve.

Sophie wanted to find out if the volume of water she used made a difference, so she did the same thing with different volumes. The table shows her results.

Volume of water (ml)	Number of scoops of sugar that dissolved
20	5
40	9
60	16
80	20

1. a) Should Sophie draw a **bar chart** or a **line graph** to show her results?

_____

b) Explain your answer to part **a)**. _____

_____

2. Which **variables** did Sophie have to keep the same to make her test fair?

_____

Sophie decided to check her results by repeating her whole investigation twice. The table shows all her results.

| Volume of water (ml) | Number of scoops of sugar that dissolved | | | Average |
	1st go	2nd go	3rd go	
20	5	6	4	5
40	9	10	11	
60	16	14	15	
80	20	21	19	

Look again at the table at the bottom of page 24. Sophie worked out the **average** number of scoops for each volume of water. She added her three results together and divided by three. Using the average result is better than just using one result.

3. Write a **conclusion** for Sophie's first investigation.

_____

_____

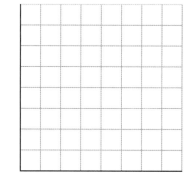

4. Work out the averages for the rest of Sophie's results and write them in the table on page 24.

5. Show Sophie's average results on this grid.

Kofi wanted to find out if the kind of **solid** used made a difference. The table shows the results of his investigation. He found that the amount of solid that dissolved depended on what the solid was.

Material	Number of scoops that dissolved
salt	4
sugar	21
baking soda	1
washing soda	3

6. a) Should Kofi draw a **bar chart** or a **line graph** to show his results?

_____

b) Explain your answer to part **a)**.

_____

7. Kofi tested each material once. How could he have got better results?

_____

_____

Changing materials

Tom mixed some different materials:

1 **Sand and water.** Tom separated the sand from the water again by **filtering** the **mixture**.
2 **Vinegar and bicarbonate of soda.** The mixture made bubbles of **gas**. Tom could not separate the vinegar and bicarbonate of soda again.
3 **Salt and water.** Tom separated the salt from the water again by **evaporation**. He heated the mixture to evaporate the water and leave the salt behind.
4 **Cement powder and water.** The mixture set into a hard **solid**. Tom could not separate the water and cement powder.

Some materials change when they are mixed. Sometimes there is a **reversible change**, which means that you can get the original materials back again. A change where a new material is made is an **irreversible change** and you cannot get the original materials back.

I. a) Which mixtures that Tom made were in a **state** that is reversible?

(You can just give the numbers.) _____

b) Explain how you worked out your answer to part **a)**.

_____

Heating and cooling materials can also make them change. Charlotte heated some different materials. The table shows her results.

Material	What happened when it was heated
ice	The ice melted and turned into liquid water.
water	The water evaporated and turned into water vapour.
egg	The clear part of the egg turned white and the yolk became hard.
chocolate	The chocolate melted and turned into a liquid.
cake mixture	The mixture stopped being runny.

Changing ice into water is a **reversible change**, because you can change the water back into ice by cooling it down.

Heating an egg is an **irreversible change**, because when you have cooked an egg you cannot change it back into a raw egg again.

Cooling materials usually causes reversible changes. For example, cooling **water vapour** makes it condense into **liquid** water (**condensation**). You can get water vapour back again by letting the water evaporate.

2. a) What happens when you heat chocolate?

_____

b) What will happen to the runny chocolate if you cool it down?

_____

c) Does heating chocolate cause a reversible or an irreversible change?

_____

3. Write down two materials from the table that are changed irreversibly when they are heated. _____

4. a) What is the reverse of **evaporating**? _____

b) What is the reverse of **freezing**? _____

Did you know? We cook food to make it taste better, but cooking also makes food safer. The heat kills micro-organisms in the food that could make you ill.

Burning

Some materials burn when they are heated. You can usually see a flame when something is **burning**. Burning is an **irreversible change** and forms new materials.

When wood burns, it changes into ash and invisible **gases** are given off while it is burning.

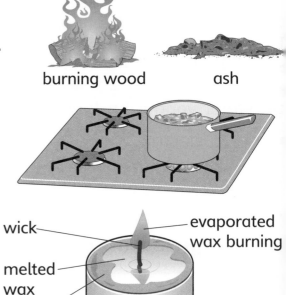

burning wood   ash

Burning can be a useful change. For example, some cookers use a gas called natural gas. When this gas burns, it changes into different, invisible gases. It also gives out a lot of heat while it is burning, which we can use for cooking or for heating our homes.

Candles are made of wax. When the wax is heated, it **melts** and evaporates. It is the **evaporating** gas that burns, not the wick.

wick — evaporated wax burning

melted wax

wax

1. How can you tell if a material is burning?

_____

2. What new materials are formed when wood burns?

_____

3. Write down two ways that burning can be useful.

_____

4. When you light a candle, there are some **reversible changes** and an irreversible change.

a) What are the reversible changes?

_____

b) What is the irreversible change?

_____

Burning

Burning can also be dangerous. Burning materials give out a lot of heat, which can hurt you or even kill you. Breathing the smoke from a fire can make you ill or kill you and some materials also give off poisonous **gases** when they burn.

There are some simple rules you can follow to prevent fires:
- never play with matches
- do not put clothes or toys near heaters or fires because if these things get too hot they may start to burn
- unplug electrical things when you have finished using them.

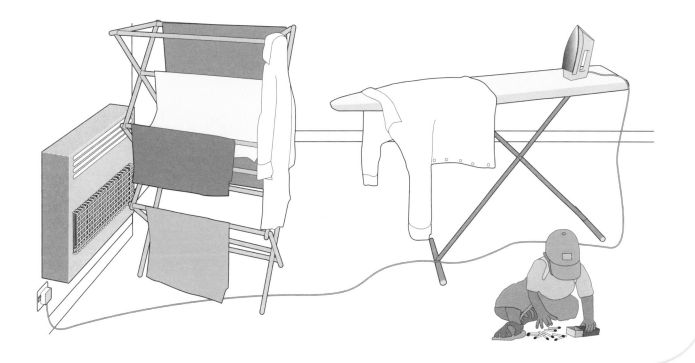

5. Some things shown in the picture could be dangerous. Write down three things you can see that might start a fire.

_____

_____

_____

Did you know? More people die in the UK each year from breathing smoke than are killed by the heat of the fire. Smoke alarms can detect smoke from a fire and warn people to get out of the building.

Scientific investigation

In this book you have found out how materials can be changed. For example, changes to materials include changing state and dissolving. You have also learnt how to ask scientific questions. Good scientists need many different skills in order to investigate things. You can learn some of the other skills you need in the other **Understanding Science** books. The table below shows you the skills you need and which books help to teach you these skills or give you practice in using them.

Skill	Book pages					
	Animals & Plants	Our Bodies	Using Materials	Changing Materials	Forces & Electricity	Light, Sound & Space
Planning an investigation						
Asking a scientific question			10		6	
Knowing what variables are	6–7			8, 22, 24		8–9, 14
Planning a fair test	6–7		10–11, 20–21	8–9	6–7, 12	8–9, 14
Predicting what you think you will find out		28–29			6–7	14
Recording and presenting your evidence						
Making tally charts		27				
Drawing pictograms		8				
Drawing bar charts		8, 27	12–13, 20	22–23, 24–25		
Drawing line graphs		28–29		10, 22–23, 24–25	17, 19	8–9
Considering your evidence and evaluating it						
Writing a conclusion	6–7	9	12–13, 20	9, 10, 25	7, 13, 17–19	
Evaluating your investigation	6–7	9, 26	13	9, 10	13, 17	15

Answers

ges 4
5

1. Solid and liquid.

2. a) Melting.
   b) Freezing, solidifying.

3. Heat from the air in the kitchen warms them up so they melt.

4. a) Cool it down (freeze it).
   b) 0°C

5. a) It is not usually hot enough.
   b) Heat it up (or make it warmer).

6. The air is cooler than 1000°C, so the lava cools down and solidifies.

ges 6
7

1. Evaporating.

2. Evaporation happens faster when it is warm.

3. Jake.

4. a) Liquid.
   b) Gas.

5. Water in the paint evaporates.

6. You can smell the liquid that has evaporated and turned into gas.

ges 8
9

1. Temperature, area, wind.

2. Will is going to measure the volume. Jane is only looking at her paper towels.

3. The temperature and whether or not there was a breeze.

4. The paper towel that was spread out dried the fastest.

5. The water in the tub with the large area evaporated faster than the water in the tub with a small area.

6. The test was fair because both tubs were kept at the same temperature and in the same place (so any breeze would have been the same).
   You could also have said that Will must be very careful not to spill any of the water when he is pouring it.

Answers

Page 10   **1.**

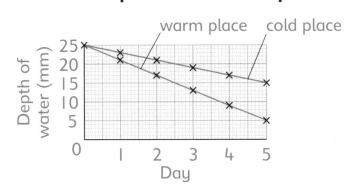

How temperature affects evaporation

2. The water evaporated faster from the jar that was kept in the warm place.

3. The test was fair because Becky used the same size and shape jars and she started with the same amount of water in each jar.

4. a) Yes.
   b) The jar that Becky left in a cold place had less water at the end, so some of it must have evaporated.
   You could also have said that puddles dry up even on cold days, so water must be evaporating.

Page 11   **1.** Warmth, a bigger area, a breeze.

2. It blows air, and also warms the air.

3. a) B
   b) It has a bigger area.

Pages 12   **1. a)** Condensation.
and 13   **b)** Evaporation.

2. It has evaporated from the water in the pans.

3. The window is cold. Water vapour in the air cools down when it is near the window, then it condenses to make drops of liquid water.

4. The windows are not cold enough in summer to make water vapour condense.

5. The cold can cools down water vapour that is already in the air and makes it condense into drops of liquid water.

Page 15   **1. a)** It evaporates.
   b) Water could evaporate from rivers or lakes.

2. It forms clouds.

3. It runs into rivers and eventually goes back to the sea.

4. The same bit of water can go round and round.

5. Two from: rivers, reservoirs, wells.

ges 16
1 17
1. a) Freezing (or solidifying).
   b) Condensing.
   c) Melting.
   d) Evaporating.

2. a) Heat it (melt it).
   b) Cool it down again (freeze it).

3. a) 0°C
   b) 100°C
   c) 0°C (This is because liquid water can evaporate at any temperature.)

4. a) It stays the same.
   b) It stays the same.

5. Water vapour.

ges 18
1 19
1. a) By using your fingers.
   b) The grains of sand are too small.

2. The holes in the sieve are too big.

3. The grains of sand are too big to go through the holes in the paper.

4. a) ... the bits of flour are small enough to go through the holes in the sieve and the peas are too big to go through the holes.
   b) ... the bits of flour and the bits of sand are both small enough to go through the holes in the sieve.

ges 20
1 21
1. a) Solution.
   b) Transparent (it looks just like water).

2. You cannot see through the mixture.

3.

Mixture	What is left in the filter paper	What goes through the filter paper
sugar and water	nothing	sugar and water
sand and water	sand	water
flour and water	flour	water
salt and water	nothing	salt and water

4. a) It dissolves.
   b) The salt is in tiny pieces that go through the holes in the filter paper.

5. a) No.
   b) Only the water evaporates from the solution, not the salt, so the condensed water on the tile does not have any salt in it.

Pages 22 and 23

1. The temperature and the size of the pieces.

2. If she stirred and the size of the pieces.

3. You should have crossed out: not stirring, bigger, colder.

4. a) Bar chart.
   b) She can describe the variable that she changed in words.
   c)

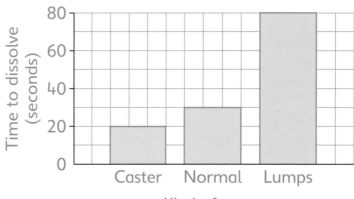

Dissolving different kinds of sugar

5. a) Line graph.
   b) Temperature can be shown by a number and there are numbers between his measurements that mean something.
   c)

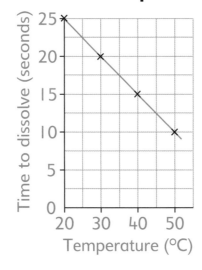

Dissolving salt at different temperatures

Answers

1. a) Line graph.

   b) The volume can be shown by numbers and there are numbers in between Sophie's measurements.

2. Temperature, stirring, size of the pieces.

3. The greater the volume of water, the more sugar dissolves in it.

4.

Volume of water (ml)	Average
20	5
40	10
60	15
80	20

5.

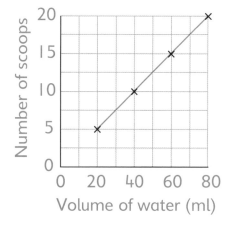

6. a) Bar chart.

   b) The variable he changed (the material) is described in words.

7. Test each material three times and find the average number of scoops.

1. a) 1 and 3

   b) Tom could separate the parts of the mixture again.

2. a) It melts.

   b) It will solidify again.

   c) Reversible.

3. Egg, cake mixture.

4. a) Condensing.

   b) Melting.

1. You can see a flame.

2. Ash, invisible gases.

3. Cooking, heating (**or** light).

4. a) Melting wax, evaporating wax.

   b) Burning.

5. Playing with matches, putting clothes near the fire, leaving the iron on.

Index and glossary